THE G!DDY LIM!T

NOT QUITE TENTH ANNIVERSARY BOOK

by Alex Leonard

Published by The Orcadian (Kirkwall Press)
Hell's Half Acre, Hatston, Kirkwall, Orkney, KW15 1GJ
Tel. 01856 879000 • Fax 01856 879001 • www.orcadian.co.uk

Book sales: www.orcadian.co.uk/shop/index.php

ISBN 978-1-902957-69-2

Printed in Orkney by The Orcadian, Hatston Print Centre, Hell's Half Acre, Hatston, Kirkwall, Orkney, KW15 1GJ

THE G!DDY LIM!T

NOT QUITE TENTH ANNIVERSARY BOOK

Alex

FOR MUM & DAD

INTRODUCTION

The plan – forged back in 2010 – was spectacularly simple: Every five years we would release a Giddy Limit book compiling the weekly strips from *The Orcadian*. We would launch with a Fifth Anniversary volume, followed five years later by a (wait for it) Tenth Anniversary volume… and so on. But then, most inconveniently, the first book sold out a year early. Thanks Orkney. Thanks a lot.

So instead here we are lumbered with the snappily-titled The Giddy Limit Not Quite Tenth Anniversary Book. Picking up exactly where the last book left off, there are over 200 strips reprinted herein covering the highs and lows of life on our beloved islands over the last four years – Wheelie-BinGate, radon gas scares, The Crankshaft Scandal, flash floods, heat waves and the mother-of-all northern lights displays that brought all who witnessed it to their knees – you can relive it all here.

Also included in this volume is the artwork from four years' worth of The Giddy Limit calendars. I have had a lot of fun working on these each year, and over time the subject matter has developed into what is now out-and-out parody of some of my favourite genres in pop culture and is pure indulgence on my part. I am delighted to have been given the space to reprint them here larger than they originally appeared in the calendars themselves, where often much of the detail was unfortunately lost.

So I do hope you enjoy this collection, but ideally not too speedily. Try and make it last, say, six years or so. That would lessen the need to come up with another overly-complicated title for the next volume.

Alex Leonard

October 2014

FOREWORD

Behold anither masterpiece
A book tae top the chart
A crafted mix, a synthesis
O' literature and art.

The subject metter is unique
The product weel bespoke
A topic that we all howld dear
Wur islands and wur folk.

Hid cleverly encapsulates
The nub o' Orkney life
The essence o' wur culture
So hid's Orkneyism rife.

The message in each sketch and skit
A smirk or smile compels
And of coorse bae laughan at hid
Wur laughan at wursels.

Hid's universal in appeal
And sure will satisfy
All Orkney folk and incomers
And uncan folk forby.

For birthday gift or Christmas treat
The very thing ye need o'
For owld and young and in atween
Tae hiv a peedie read o'.

There is a laugh in every line
And every picter in it
All I can say is "Alex beuy"
"Thoo are the Giddy Limit."

Harvey Johnston

SANDY LIZ CHI

DAVO

IVY

2010 CALENDAR

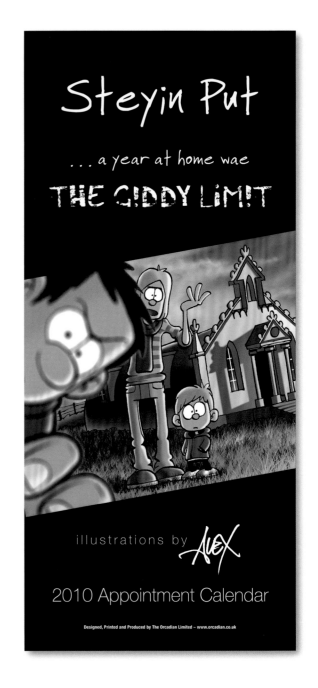

Broad Street – Hogmanay: Ah'm telt I had a good night...

St. John's Head, Hoy: Apparently hid's hard no tae lukk faerd when perched a thoosand feet above sea level...

Hivvan a peedie rest oan wir wey tae the Black Craig.
We had quite a few more actually...

The Brough o' Birsay: I must mind oan tae
check the tide times in future...

Lukkin' fur Primula Scotica at Yesnaby.

Scapa Beach, June: Still a bit early fur sweeman I doot...

Orphir Round Kirk: Cheemo's "game" got a bit oot o' hand...

Sunset at The Ring o' Brodgar: This proved tae be the last time I ivver asked Davo tae takk a photo...

A beautiful, still evening in Rackwick. Perfect fur eating ootdoors. If ye're a midge.

Dusk at the Italian Chapel. I still hivna quite figured oot hoo tae wirk that stupeed timer...

Stromness. Makkin' wir wey towards the Sooth End.
Hid wis bonny when we left the North End...

Sledging at Brinkie's Brae. Hid wid seem we
mibbe over-buffed Cheemo's sledge...

This strip ran during the week that T*scos was closed for its refurbishment.

The queue really was that big. Honest.

2011 CALENDAR

ORKNEY *for* HOLIDAYS

HOY SOUND
THE GATEWAY TO A HAPPY HOLIDAY

RETURN FARES

FIRST CLASS	SECOND CLASS	THIRD CLASS
4/6	3/6	3/-

STENNESS

HISTORIC CENTRE OF A MOST BEAUTIFUL COUNTY

Illustrated Holiday Booklet and if desired Lodgings Guide. Post free to Passenger Manager, Dept A2, Shanders Coaches Ltd, Orkney

THE BAY O' SKAILL

BREEZY AND BRACING

COACH SERVICES AND FARES FROM  STATIONS, OFFICES AND AGENCIES

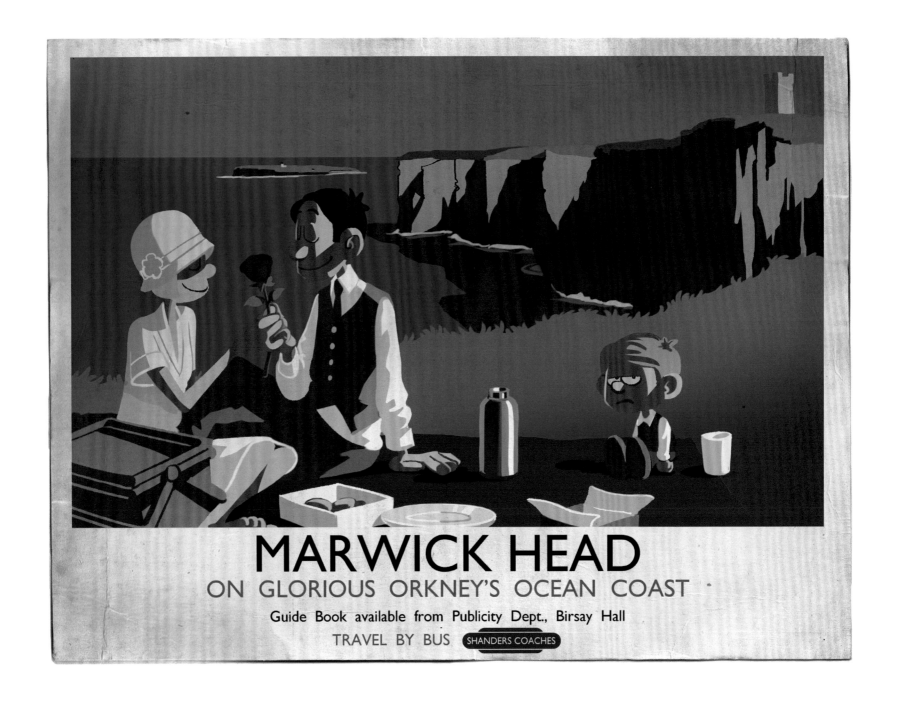

WAULKMILL BAY

Glorious Sands   Ideal Bathing

TRAVEL BY BUS   

Here's another little bit of text that is slightly meaningless

And hey by jingo here is another one

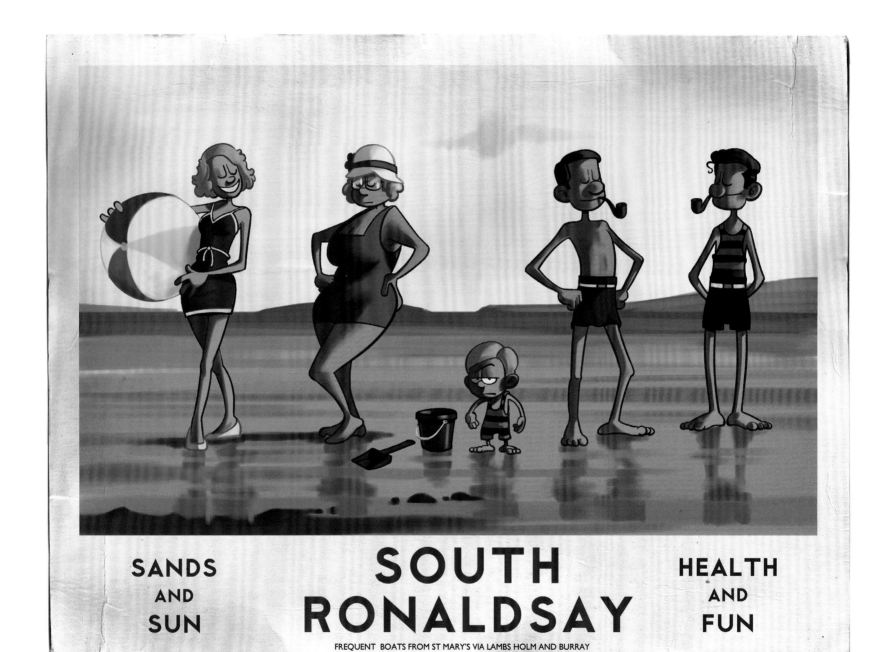

SANDS AND SUN

SOUTH RONALDSAY

HEALTH AND FUN

FREQUENT BOATS FROM ST MARY'S VIA LAMBS HOLM AND BURRAY

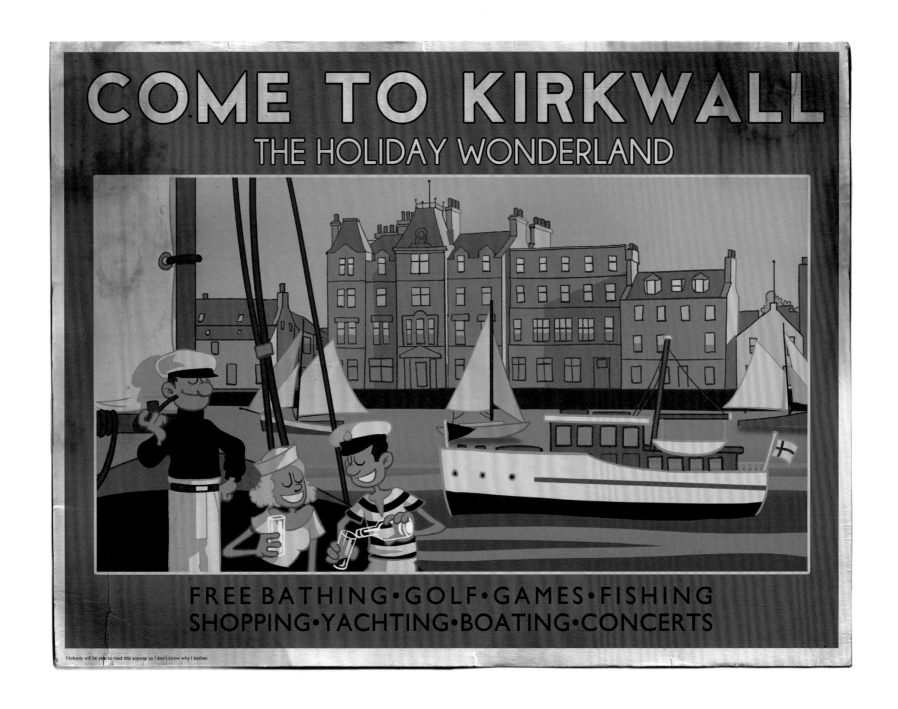

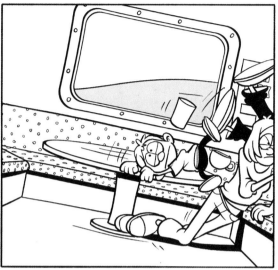

HI LIZ.

OH, HELLO THERE.

WHO WIS THAT?

JUST A FRIEND OF MINE.

A REAL FRIEND?

LORD, NO. JUST A FACEBOOK FRIEND.

AH'M THINKAN I MIGHT TAKK STEPS TAE FINALLY IMPROVE THE DRAINAGE DOON IN THE MEEDO THIS YEAR...

WEEL *THERE'S* AN IDEA...

HAS THE POSTIE BEEN THE DAY MITHER? IS ME NEW BIKE HERE? IS HID? IS HID?

NO, CHEEMO, I'M SORRY. WE ONLY ORDERED IT YESTERDAY. IT COULD TAKE ANOTHER SIX OR EIGHT WEEKS.

SIX OR EIGHT *WEEKS?* THAT'S *INSANE!* NEEBODY KIN BE EXPECTED TAE WAIT *THAT* LONG!? AH'LL LOSE ME *MIND* MITHER! THIS IS SO *UNFAIR!!*

DON'T BE SILLY. YOU JUST NEED TO LEARN A LITTLE *PATIENCE*, CHEEMO.

HMMPH. PATIENCE ISNO A VIRTUE. HID'S JIST ANITHER FORM O' DESPAIR *DISGUISED* AS A VIRTUE...

SORRY TAE BUTHER YE, SANDY BELLY—I FUND TWA THINGS STREWN ABOOT THE MEEDO EFTER THE STORMS LAST WEEK...

DIS ANY O HID BELONG TAE *YOU?*

2012 CALENDAR

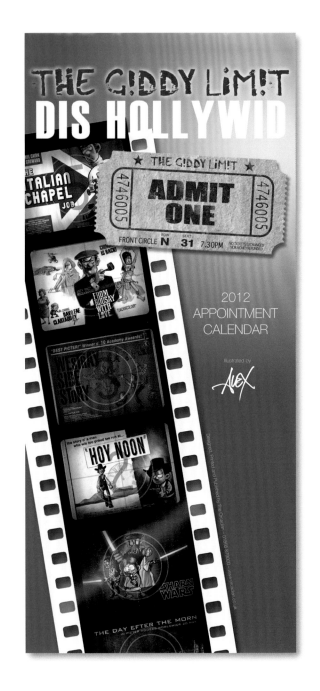

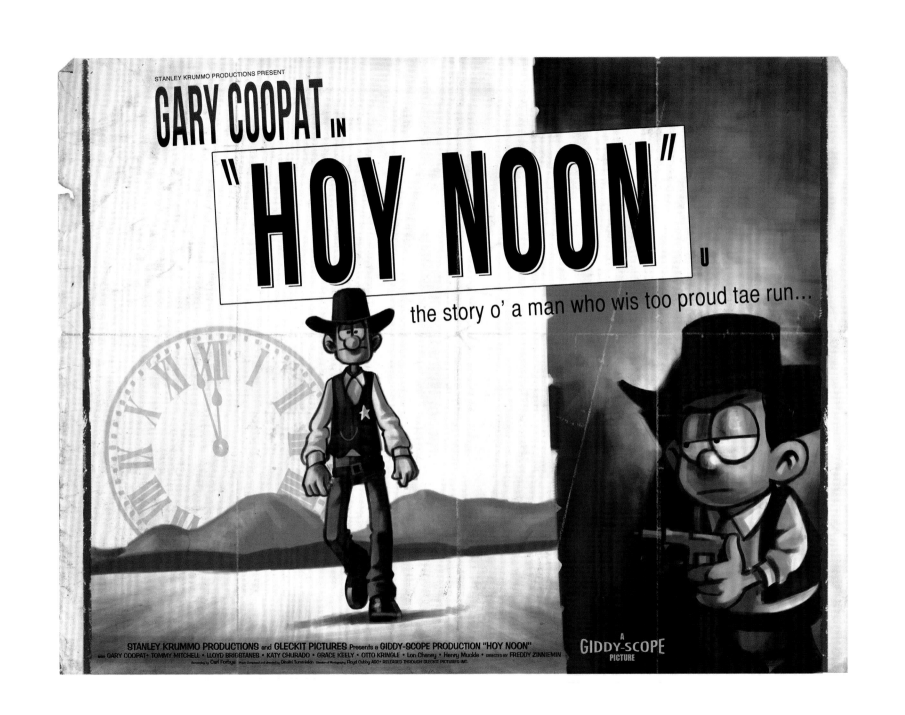

74

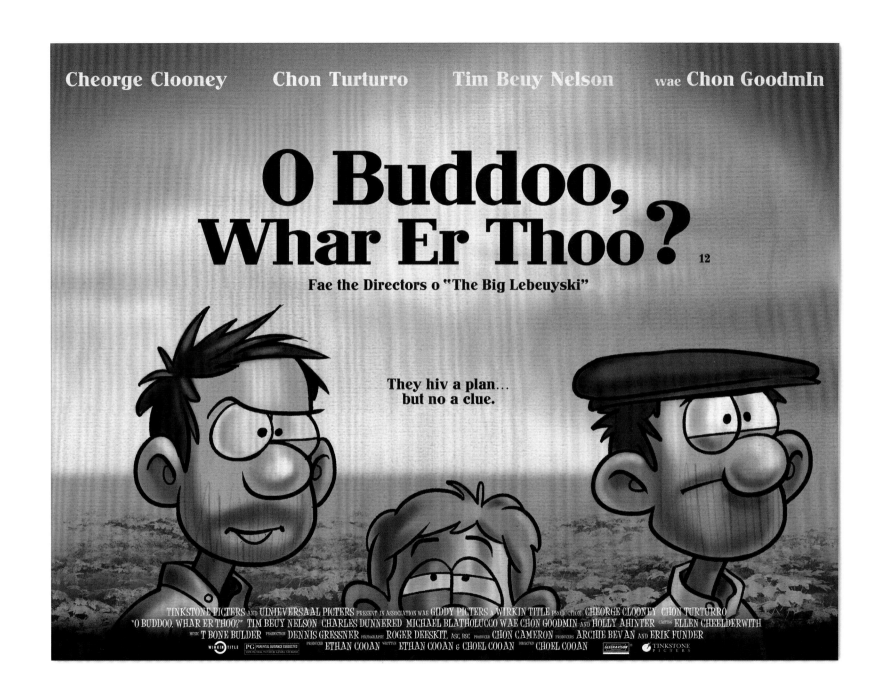

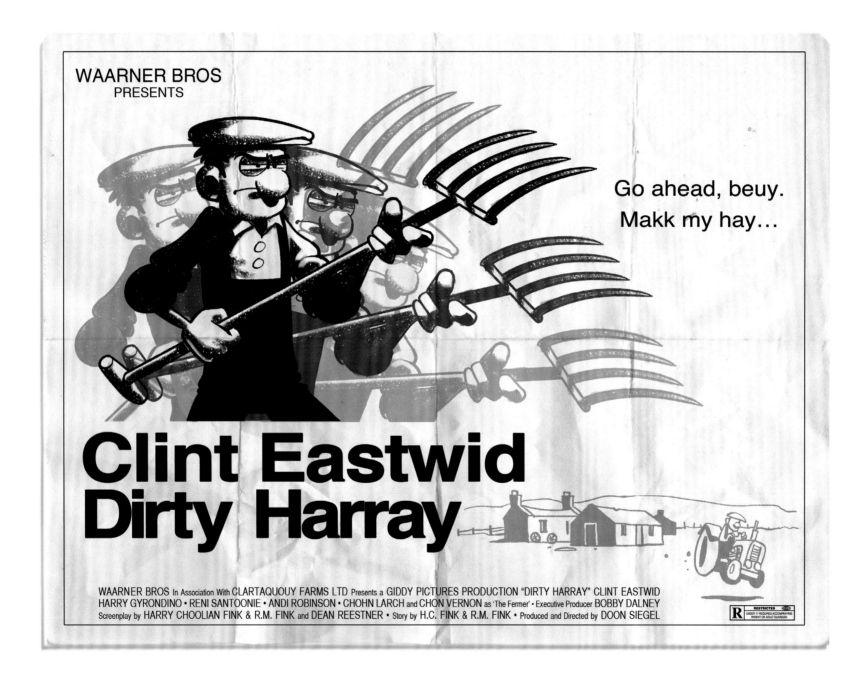

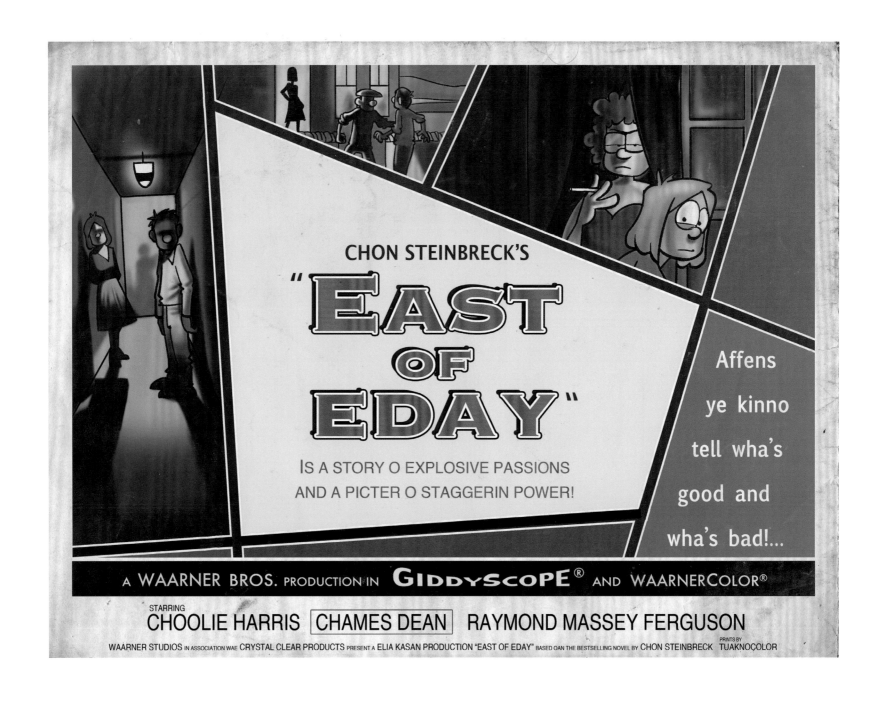

"aall aboot evie"

hid's aall aboot weeman... and thir men!

BETTY DAVIS
ANNE BONXIE
CHEORGE SANDERS
CELESTE HOLM
AALL ABOOT EVIE

Gary Mildroo • Hugh Matlo

Thelma Ritto • Marilyn Moanroe

Gregory Ratoff • Barbara Baest

Waalter Hampden

Produced by DIMMLE F ZANUCK
Directed by CHOSEPH MANKIEBITS

"BEST PICTER!" Winner o' 10 Academy Awaards!

WESTRAY SIDE STORY

GIDDY PICTURES PRESENTS
"WESTRAY SIDE STORY"
A BOBBY WISE PRODUCTION
STARRING NATALIE WID

RICHARD BYREMER   RUSS TAMBO
RITA MORENO   CHEORGE CHAKIRIS
DIRECTED BY BOBBY WISE   SCREENPLAY BY ERNEST LIMMER
ASSOCIATE PRODUCER SAUL CHIRPAN   CHOREOGRAPHY BY CHEROME ROBBINS
MUSIC BY LINNARD BERNSTEIN   LYRICS BY STEVIE SOONDHEIM
PRESENTED BY GIDDY PICTERS INC. IN ASSOCIATION WAE PHEONIX CINEMA. RELEASED BY UNKAN ARTISTS

WHIT A SURPRISE.

YET ANITHER RAINY DAY.

2012 SUCKS SO FAR!!

I OFTEN WINDER, DAVO, WHY DAE YOU FERMERS **BUTHER** MAKKIN SCARECROWS? EVERYWAN KIN SEE THEY DON'T ACTUALLY WIRK - JUST **LUKK!** I MEAN, WHIT PURPOSE DAE THEY REALLY SERVE?

THIR ARE SOME QUESTIONS THAT JIST SHOULDNA BE ASKED...

EH?

SOME SECRETS, SANDY, ARE BETTER LEFT BURIED...

OKAY YIR SCARIN ME NOO DAVO...

SO IT IS WRITTEN, SO SHALL IT BE...

Probably one of the oddest strips I have written. I'm not sure it ever made much sense. But scarecrows don't scare birds away, so there must be some other reason farmers use them...

86

This was printed the week when in an episode of The Simpsons it was announced that Groundskeeper Willie in fact grew up in Kirkwall. The reference may well have escaped many readers at the time.

A tribute to our little cat Esme who passed away that week. It's actually a Sigmund Freud quote.

I try not to hide away from politics, but I'll happily hide from a politician.

Sometimes Orkney writes the strips for me.

London 2012.

Not so much "Davo in his shed with a cow", more "me in my office with my cat".

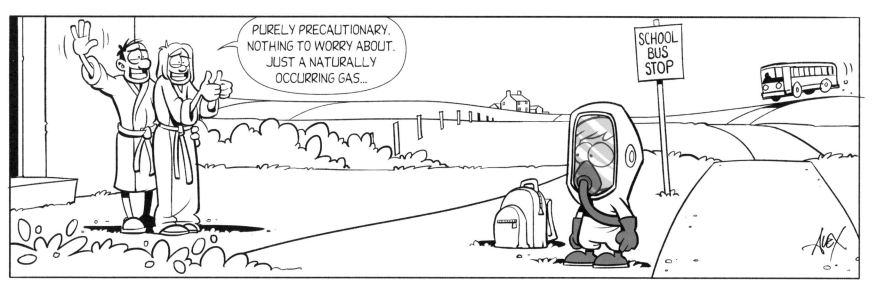

The Radon gas 'scare'. Remember that?

I've written many strips about the wind in Orkney, but this was by far the most fun to draw.

24 HR CASH POINT

Transaction complete. Would you like an advice slip?

Yes   No

24 HR CASH POINT

Transaction complete. Would you like an advice slip?

Yes   No

****
Purple really isn't your colour...
****

AYE AYE DAVO. WHIT LIKE?

GRAND. WHIT LIKE YERSEL?

NO BAD. JIST BEEN WIRK—

MERCY ME...

HID GETS DARK RIGHT **QUEEK** NOO, EH?

ANY IDEAS WHAT YOU MIGHT WANT FOR CHRISTMAS THIS YEAR?

SORRY. NUTHEEN REALLY SPRINGS TAE MIND, NO.

I THINK YOU ARE DRINKING TOO MUCH COLA, CHEEMO. I MEAN... DID YOU KNOW THAT A **TOOTH** LEFT IN A GLASS OF COKE WILL EVENTUALLY **DISSOLVE**!?

AND THAT IT IS ACIDIC ENOUGH TO WASH **BLOOD** OFF A **PAVEMENT**!?

AWESOME!

ANOTHER EPIC FAIL. I THINK I AM GETTING PROGRESSIVELY **WORSE** AT PARENTING...

Parts of Kirkwall flooded in Christmas 2012.

2013 CALENDAR

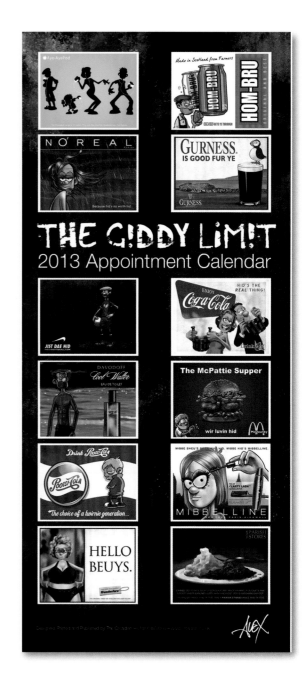

Made in Scotland from Farmers

HOM-BRU **GETS YE THROUGH**

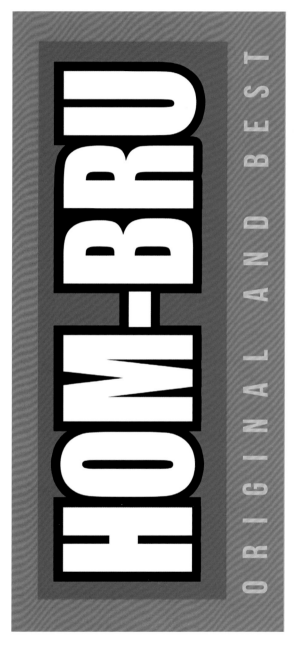

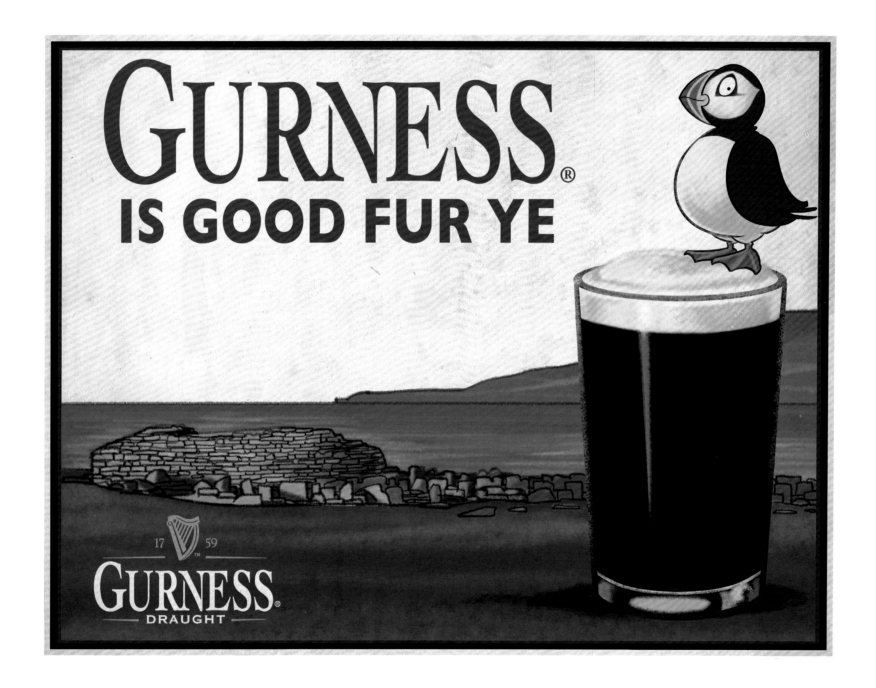

116

119

HELLO BEUYS.

THE WAN AND AOWNLY
Dunderbra®

THE ORIGINAL OWER-THE-SHOULDER BOULDER-HOLDER

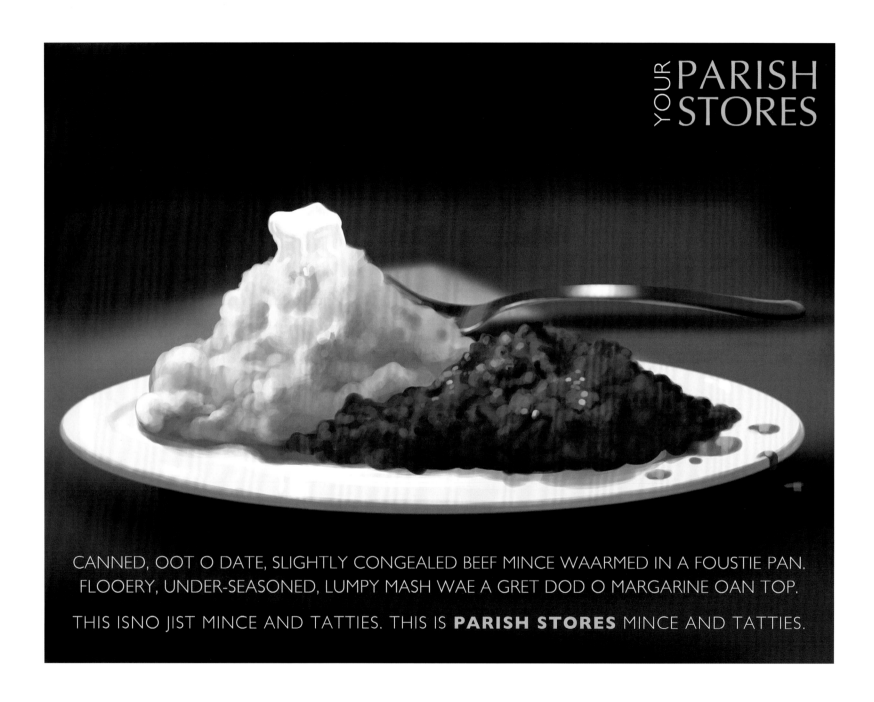

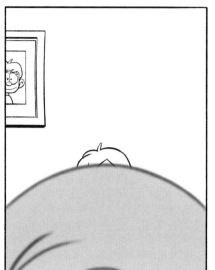

YOU'VE OVER-EATEN. YET AGAIN.

HID'S JUST A GUESS, BUT AH'M FERLY SURE YIR PULLIN A FACE I'D RATHER NO SEE ANYWEY...

I DON'T FEEL LIKE GAAN TAE SCHOOL THE DAY. I THINK I HIV THE FLU.

REALLY? WHAT ARE YOUR SYMPTOMS?

MY SYMPTOMS ARE THAT I DON'T FEEL LIKE GAAN TAE SCHOOL TODAY.

SO... WHIT- NOO SHE'S A *DOCTOR*...?

My hookers hid wis wild that night.

Every. Damn. Year.

Wheelie-BinGate.

I don't really.

Once, a ferry's crankshaft broke and a lot of folk got really, really angry about it.

134

136

Downloading... 16%

Downloading... 16%

Downloading... 16%

Downloading... 17%

141

REMEMBER - TO BE FULLY APPLYING YOURSELF YOU SHOULD BE ASKING: "WHAT EXACTLY CAN I GET OUT OF SCHOOL EACH DAY?"

I TEND TAE BE MORE BUTHERED ABOOT **WHEN** EXACTLY CAN I GET OOT O SCHOOL EACH DAY...

SO I DOOT AH'LL JIST HIV TAE ORDER ANITHER WAN. I MEAN HID'S CLEARLY FAALTY, BUT WHIN KIN YE DAE? AS THE SAYING GOES: "THE CUSTOMER IS NIVVER RIGHT."

THAT'S NOT HOW THE SAYING GOES. NOT AT **ALL**...

WHO TAUGHT YE **THAT**, BEUY?

Thank You For Shopping At Parish St...

144

BUILT ME FIRST AWESOME SNOWMAN O THE YEAR AND HID'S AOWNLY NOVEMBER!

ACH... AH'M FOOLIN NOBODY.

ACTUALLY KIN WE GO TAE THE ITHER WAN UP THE STREET? I PREFER HID THERE.

SURE, NO PROBLEM.

SO... LIKE... DOES THIS OTHER PLACE HAVE BETTER CAKES? OR BETTER COFFEE?

BETTER GOSSIP.

It's the only part anyone knows...

2014 CALENDAR

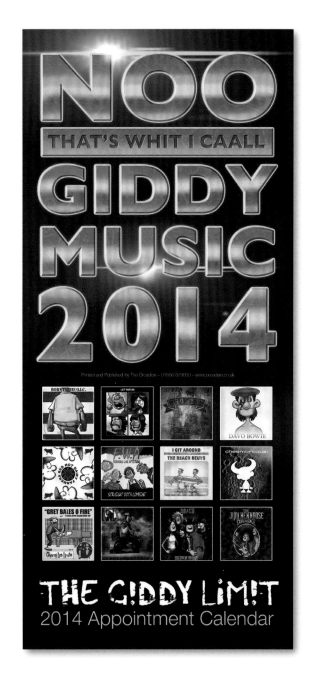

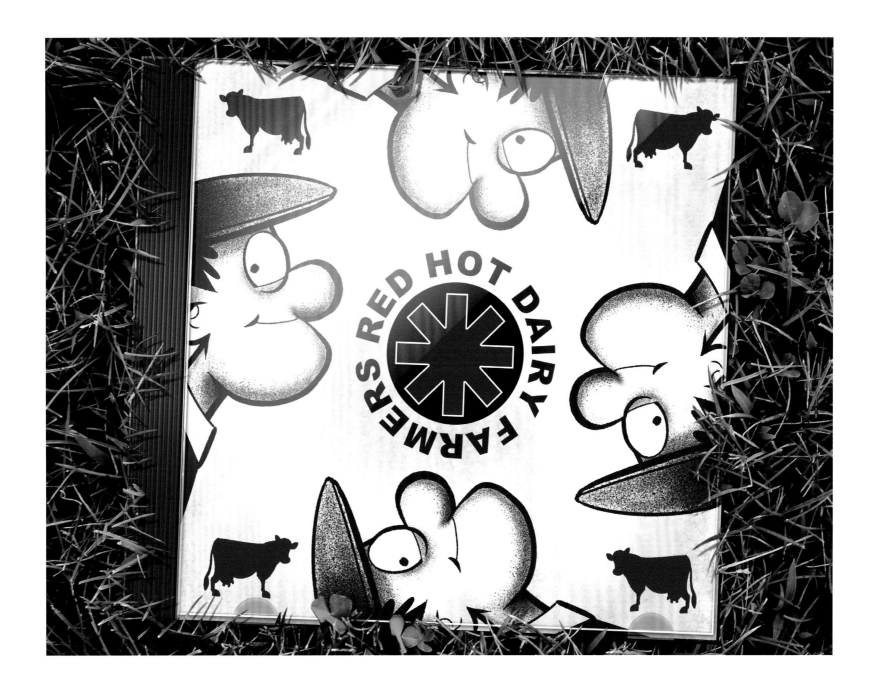

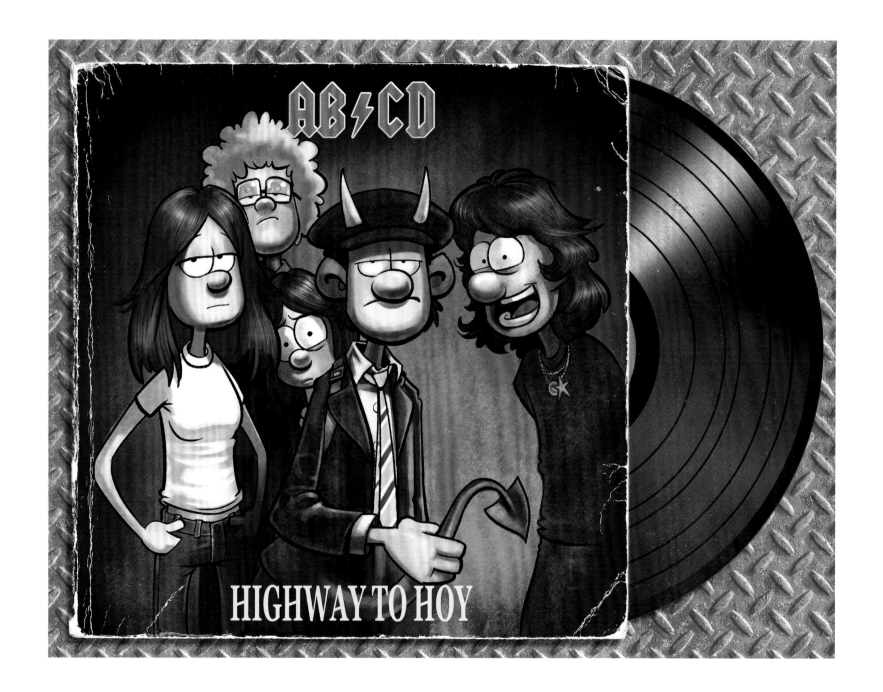

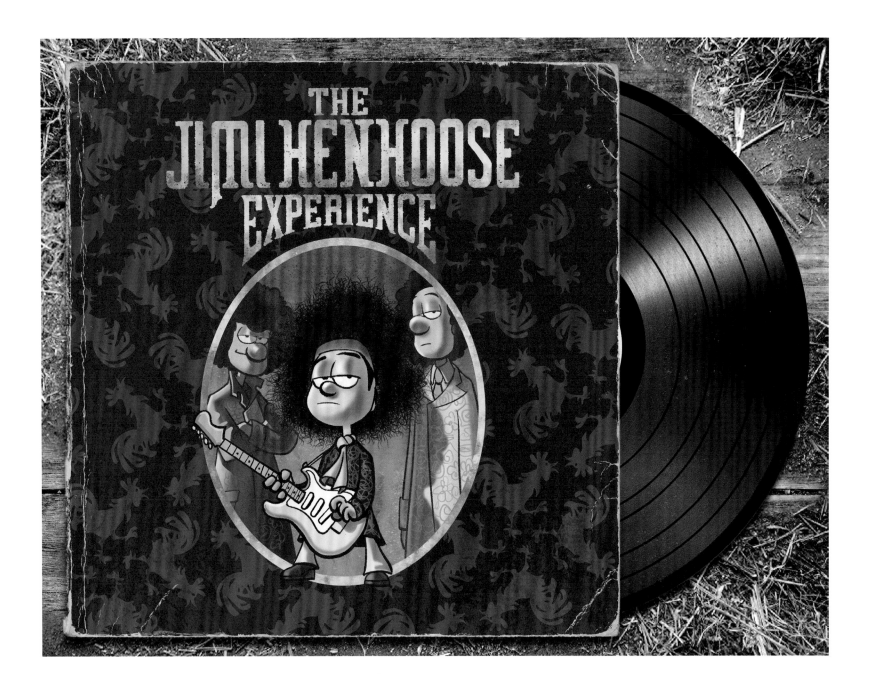

165

I still get compliments about this strip. It struck a chord with a lot of people…

You can always count on a slurry spreader to ruin a nice day.

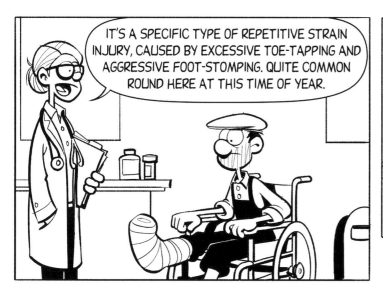

I had walked the beautiful Black Craig route that week and had checked my phone for messages along the way. I hated myself for doing so.

Every group of friends has to suffer an Ivy in their Facebook feed. If you don't, then you are probably the Ivy.